This book belongs to...

D0259577

First published 1999 by Walker Books Ltd
87 Vauxhall Walk, London SE11 5HJ

4 6 8 10 9 7 5 3

© 1999 Lucy Cousins

Printed in Italy

British Library Cataloguing in Publication Data
A catalogue record for this book is available from the British Library.

ISBN 0-7445-6923-0

Maisy's Favourite Things Colouring Book

by Lucy Cousins

WALKER BOOKS
AND SUBSIDIARIES
LONDON • BOSTON • SYDNEY

Maisy likes playing in her sandpit

Maisy rides her trike

Maisy kicks
her ball

Maisy cuddles Teddy

Maisy likes
rain

Maisy likes flowers

drives the train

Maisy likes to swing

Maisy likes her rocking horse

Maisy likes riding

in the tractor

Maisy splashes in the bath

Maisy likes making pictures

Help Maisy
make pictures

good party

Here are some more books about the lovable mouse called Maisy, all drawn by Lucy Cousins!

Another Colouring Book

Maisy and Her Friends   0-7445-6924-9

Board Books

Count with Maisy   0-7445-5221-4
Maisy's Colours   0-7445-2222-2

Lift-the-Flap Board Books

Where is Maisy?   0-7445-6919-2
Where is Maisy's Panda?   0-7445-6920-6

Mix-and-Match Book

Maisy's Mix-and-Match Mousewear   0-7445-6917-6

Sticker Books

Dress Maisy   0-7445-6921-4
Maisy's Day   0-7445-6922-2

Lift-the-Flap, Pull-the-Tab Books

Happy Birthday, Maisy   0-7445-6114-0
Maisy at the Farm   0-7445-6113-2
Maisy Goes to Bed   0-7445-0429-5
Maisy Goes Swimming   0-7445-0428-7
Maisy Goes to Playschool   0-7445-2506-3
Maisy Goes to the Playground   0-7445-2507-1
Maisy's ABC   0-7445-3229-9

Pop-Up Play Book

Maisy's House   0-7445-4412-2